ARCH
ADDICTS
· *Official Map Of* ·
AMBRIDGE

A guide to the Farms,
Houses & other landmarks
of Britain's best known village

Ambridge Hall

Ambridge Hall was built in the 1860s by the Lawson-Hope family as a home for the village doctor. It was once an ugly house incongruous in its rural surroundings, but its yellow brick has mellowed with age and now, in its mature garden, it has a certain Victorian charm. Its wooden shutters lend it an air of style. There are six bedrooms and a quaint staircase leading to what were originally the servants' quarters.

Laura Archer bought the property from Jack Woolley in 1973. She lived at the Hall with her lodger, Colonel Danby, and intended to bequeath it to him. However, after her death in 1985 it was discovered that Laura had not signed the top copy of her will. The Hall was inherited by Laura's niece in New Zealand who put it up for sale the following year. It was bought by incomers Lynda and Robert Snell. Life in Ambridge would never be the same again!

April Cottage

This is the home of Martha Woodford, who used to run the village shop until she retired and handed over the reins to Betty Tucker. Martha acts as caretaker of Ambridge's red telephone box, which she keeps well polished, and occasionally she babysits for Sharon Richards. She is one of the village's most informative gossips.

Arkwright Hall

Even in its heyday, Arkwright Hall was never considered an architectural masterpiece. The priest-hole discovered in the fifties is one of its few features of interest.

Charles Grenville bought the seventeeth century Hall in 1959 and turned it into a community centre for the village. The centre served a useful purpose, but the noisy youth activities held there generated controversy.

After Grenville's death in 1965 it was bought by Jack Woolley who appointed Sid Perks to run it and planned a leisure centre and swimming-pool on the site. Far from justifying such expansion, the venture proved a failure and in 1970 Jack reopened the building as a field study centre; Gordon Armstrong built up a wildfowl sanctuary on Arkwright Lake. Over the years the grounds were absorbed into what became the Country Park. Arkwright Hall fell into disrepair and is now an empty shell awaiting restoration.

Blossom Hill Cottage

Blossom Hill Cottage is a thatched, two-bedroomed cottage
with a sunny outlook and welcoming appearance; French windows
lead out of the sitting-room. Mike Daly fell in love with
the cottage and bought it from Squire Lawson-Hope in 1952.
Ralph and Lilian Bellamy bought the cottage in 1971 and let
it to Lilian's mother Peggy .

In 1982 Blossom Hill Cottage was burgled and the following
year it was badly damaged by fire. Peggy moved to The Lodge to
start her new life with Jack Woolley in 1991, and the cottage
remained empty until it was bought three years later by
Borchester solicitor, Usha Gupta, former partner of the late
Mark Hebden.

Bridge Farm

Bridge Farm is one of several on the Berrow Estate.
Primarily a dairy farm, it has 170 acres of land and a late-Victorian
red-brick farmhouse of no particular distinction. Pat and
Tony Archer have lived there since the death of the previous
tenant, Jim Elliott, in 1977. They began with the milking herd
and hens they brought from Willow Farm, but in 1984 started
to grow organic vegetables. Pat has expanded the dairy and now
organic icecream and yoghurt are produced under the Bridge
Farm label. Pat and Tony have also opened a farm shop where
they sell their produce.

Pat and Tony live at Bridge Farm with their children John,
Helen and Tommy. John is already showing entrepreneurial
skills, but to Tony's chagrin he sees Brian Aldridge as
his role model. Helen and Tommy go to Borchester Green
Comprehensive School.

Brookfield

The Archer family had been tenants on the Lawson-Hope estate for many years before 21 year old Dan Archer took over Brookfield (then a 100 acre farm) from his father in 1917. The old brick-and-timber farmhouse dates back to the sixteenth century and stands in the centre of Brook Field, one of Ambridge's four medieval open fields. (The others are West Field, Lakey Hill and East Field.) By the end of the sixties Dan had managed to bring Brookfield up to 435 acres. Faced with a heavy tax bill after the death of Dan in 1986, his son, Phil, contemplated selling Brookfield. To the relief of his wife, Jill, and indeed the nation, he found a less drastic solution. Phil and his younger son David, are now in partnership and they continue the family tradition of mixed farming.

Phil and Jill live at Brookfield, as Dan and Doris did in their day. Brookfield is the social heart of Ambridge and Jill always has the kettle on for when her numerous friends and relatives come for tea and sympathy.

A bungalow was built on the bank of the River Am in 1990 for David and Ruth Archer. They live there now with their daughter Phillipa Rose, or Pip as she is called.

The Bull

The Bull is the most famous inn in Borsetshire, where you can be assured of a warm welcome, a pint of Shires and delicious bar meals at a price you can afford. It dates from the late seventeenth century, although parts of it go back as far as the fifteenth. Legend has it that a ghostly drummer boy can be heard tapping on a back bedroom window.

The easiest way to find out most of what is going on in Ambridge is to eavesdrop on conversations in The Bull. There have been moments of high drama (such as when Sid threw Kathy out after he discovered her affair with Detective Sergeant Barry), high romance (when he persuaded her back again and kissed her in front of all their customers), and high comedy (when Eddie Grundy was sick in the piano and wasn't allowed back until he had found a replacement).

Until recently this attractive black-and-white building was the property of Peggy Archer. She put it up for sale in 1993 and offered Sid first refusal. At first it looked as though Sid would be unable to raise the necessary sum but fortunately Guy Pemberton came to his rescue with the offer of a partnership.

The Dower House

Guy Pemberton has made The Dower House his home. He is the current owner of the Berrow Estate, which includes Bridge Farm, Grange Farm and several other farms controlled by a farm manager. Unlike his predecessor, Cameron Fraser, who disappeared without a trace, leaving his affairs in confusion, Guy shows every sign of settling down in Ambridge.

Glebe Cottage

Built of mellow brick in the 1840s, Glebe Cottage is a small house with a particularly pretty country garden next to St Stephen's Church . Letty Lawson-Hope left Glebe Cottage and its 4 acres of land to Doris Archer for her lifetime, but in the early seventies Doris and Dan bought the freehold for £2000. It made a delightful retirement home for them, where, despite Dan's reluctance to withdraw from farming, they found great contentment. Doris died peacefully there. She willed the cottage to Dan for his lifetime and it then passed to Shula, their granddaughter.

Shula and her husband Mark Hebden renovated the cottage extensively but their plans for re-thatching the roof had to be postponed when the builders discovered a colony of wild bats. Since bats are a protected species the work had to wait until they moved on.

After Mark's death in a car crash in 1994 Shula remained at Glebe Cottage on her own. Her sorrow over the tragedy was eased by the discovery that she was to have Mark's child.

Grange Farm

Joe and Eddie Grundy are responsible for the mess that is
Grange Farm; but to be fair, it is one of the smaller tenant
farms on the Berrow Estate and not particularly productive.
Built on eighteenth-century foundations, it is a mixture of
crumbling brick and cracked rendering, with a wild area
outside, which Eddie's wife, Clarrie, tries to cultivate as a
garden. As they only rent the farm, Joe and Eddie don't feel
motivated to attend to its upkeep.

The Grundys are always full of schemes to add to their
income, but find it difficult to get any backers because
Ambridge knows them too well. Joe tried to sell mineral
water, but his clients objected to its brown colour. Eddie
dreamed of breeding maggots, but Clarrie put her foot down.
Clarrie works part-time at the Bull, but she has a full-time
job looking after Joe and Eddie and her two children,
William and Edward.

No. 1 The Green

This was a council house until Susan and Neil Carter bought it. They live here with their two children, Emma and Christopher. Susan works at the Estate Office and Neil is a salesman for an animal feed company. Their life changed when Susan helped her brother, Clive Horrobin, after he led an armed raid on the village post office. She was charged with seeking to pervert the course of public justice and went to prison for three months.

Grey Gables

Grey Gables, owned by Jack Woolley, is a late-Victorian mock-Gothic mansion set in 15 acres of graceful lawns and gardens with its own golf course, outdoor swimming-pool and indoor leisure complex all of which is surrounded by a large country park. It is also used as a conference and function centre. Much of its success is due to the clever management of Caroline Bone and the excellent cuisine of its chef Jean-Paul.

Jack has always enjoyed rubbing shoulders with the great, from Terry Wogan to Princess Margaret who attended an NSPCC gala dinner at Grey Gables in 1984. He proudly commemorated the Princess's visit by renaming Caroline's room 'The Royal Garden Suite'. For Caroline, Grey Gables, with all its splendour, is home.

Home Farm

Brian Aldridge acquired Home Farm, the largest farm in Ambridge, in 1975. The farmhouse, originally called Ambridge Court, was built on the foundations of the ancient Lyttleton Manor and is principally early-eighteenth century in origin. After the Second World War Ralph Bellamy converted it into flats for the workers on his surrounding estate. Brian converted it back into a house with the help of Jennifer, his wife. The farm is mainly arable, but Brian has gone in for diversification in the last few years and now farms deer, owns an artificial fishing lake and has developed 35 acres for off-road horse-riding.

Brian and Jennifer live at Home Farm together with their daughters Kate and Alice and Jennifer's daughter from her first marriage, Debbie.

Honeysuckle Cottage

In 1957 Walter Gabriel gave up his farm and moved into Honeysuckle Cottage. He bought a mini-bus and became the village carrier. When Walter died in 1988 his son Nelson took over the cottage and has remained there ever since. He runs both a wine bar and an antique shop in Borchester, and is well known for his ironic observations on daily life in Ambridge.

Keeper's Cottage

Keeper's Cottage is the home of Tom Forrest, Ambridge's oldest inhabitant. He used to be a gamekeeper and still gives advice and support to George Barford who is gamekeeper at Grey Gables. He mourns the absence of his wife Pru, in a nursing home after a severe stroke. He finds it increasingly difficult to manage on his own, but enjoys a pint of Shires and a game of dominoes in The Bull.

Lakey Hill

Lakey Hill rises 771 feet above sea level to the north-east of Ambridge. There are traces of several prehistoric burial mounds. The summit and its southern slopes belong to Brookfield, but the land is difficult to plough and the Archers use it mainly for grazing sheep.

It is one of Ambridge's most scenic areas and has given pleasure to many generations. Phil sat at the top of Lakey Hill with Grace Fairbrother on Coronation Day in 1953, roasting potatoes until four in the morning. Over twenty years later his daughter Shula stayed on the Hill till early morning with Neil Carter, watching the string of bonfires set alight in celebration of the Jubilee.

The Lodge

The Lodge was converted into a new home for Jack and Peggy Woolley after their marriage. They took great pleasure in planning the kitchen and the conservatory, and put in extra windows to create more light.

Jack and Peggy are happy together at The Lodge, which gives them a comfortable proximity to Grey Gables while preserving their independence.

Lower Loxley Hall

Lower Loxley Hall is the ancestral home of the Pargetter family. The date on the front door is 1702, and the Pargetter family tree can be traced as far back as the seventeenth century. Peacocks strut on the lawns which are surrounded by 400 acres of parkland. The gardens are said to have been laid out by Sir John Pargetter who made his fortune in colonial India.

Nigel Pargetter has done his best to enable Lower Loxley to pay its way with little support from his mother, Julia. He has had to look to his marketing manager Elizabeth Archer, for help in implementing his ideas. Their working relationship gradually developed into a love affair and they were married in September 1994.

Nightingale Farm

When Shula Hebden showed Marjorie Antrobus around Nightingale Farm in 1985 the property was badly neglected and the driveway was full of pot-holes. However, as a breeder of Afghan hounds, Marjorie's prime concern was for her 'gels'. She restored the farmhouse to its original state and converted the outbuildings into kennels.

Marjorie may be known locally as 'the dog woman', but her tweedy exterior conceals a heart of gold and a strong streak of femininity. She is a staunch supporter of the local church, enjoys male companionship and values her friendship with Guy Pemberton.

St Stephen's Church

St Stephen's, built on the site of an early-seventh-century Augustinian Church, was consecrated in 1281. It is an attractive church with elements of Late Norman, Early English and Perpendicular styles. In 1959 George and Helen Fairbrother added a stained-glass window in memory of Grace Archer.

The Stables

The Stables provide a home and income for Christine Barford (née Archer), who lives there with her husband George, the Grey Gables gamekeeper. Christine took over the running of the stables from Lilian Bellamy in 1975, the year she started riding classes for disabled children. She would like to stop teaching and concentrate on the livery side of the business.

Willow Farm

Willow Farm has not been a working farm since its land, 100 acres on the slopes of Lakey Hill, was divided between Brookfield and Home Farm in the early eighties. Bill Insley bought the farmhouse with 15 acres, and set up a joint pig venture with Neil Carter. When Bill died in 1986 he left Neil 8 acres of land and some outhouses. Mathew Thorogood bought the farmhouse and remaining acres as an investment. Mike and Betty Tucker were overjoyed when Mathew accepted their offer for the farmhouse in 1993.

The Tuckers live at Willow Farm with their two children, Roy and Brenda. Betty is the manager of the village shop and Mike has a milk round. He also rents land from Neil Carter and has developed an organic market garden.

Woodbine Cottage

One of the few remaining tied cottages in Ambridge, Woodbine Cottage was occupied by Brookfield farmworker Ned Larkin and his wife Mabel in 1967. After Ned's death his son Jethro and his family moved in from Rickyard Cottage.

When Bert Fry came to Brookfield in 1988 he and his wife lived in the cottage. Phil Archer wanted to give it to David and Ruth a year later but the Frys refused to move. Bert felt that he had to protect his image as he had become a celebrity after the publication of his sayings in the Borchester Echo. He had been photographed outside the cottage and he knew that was where his fans would expect to find him. Phil gave up and the Frys are still there.